Foundations And Challenges to
Encourage Technology-based Science

FACETS

D1448836

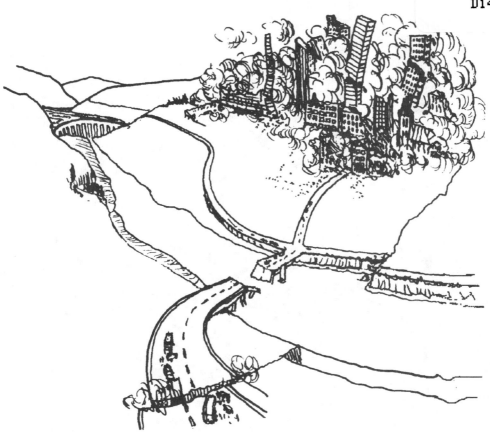

Earthquakes!

Module 1.6

The American Chemical Society

KENDALL/HUNT PUBLISHING COMPANY
4050 Westmark Drive   Dubuque, Iowa 52002

T 74870

MODULE CONTENTS

WHAT ARE THE CAUSES AND EFFECTS OF EARTHQUAKES?

What actually happens when the Earth quakes? Are earthquakes more likely to happen in some places than others? What can we do to protect ourselves from earthquakes? You are going to investigate these and other important questions about earthquakes. You will also discover some of the important science ideas that are involved.

THE **BIG** PICTURE

The idea of being in a massive earthquake is one of our worst nightmares! Like other huge natural events (hurricanes, typhoons, lightning, blizzards, storms at sea, forest and bush fires) we cannot control them. Luckily, very few of us have, or are likely to, actually experience a major earthquake.

An earthquake is the result of any movement of the Earth's crust. In fact, there are about one million earthquakes every year on planet Earth. Most of them are so tiny that we would not even notice them if we were nearby.

On average two large earthquakes happen about every two weeks. Most of these take place under the oceans and therefore do us little harm. But they can cause huge avalanches of mud and sand on the sea bed. These movements can then cause powerful underwater currents.

Most earthquakes last for less than one minute. It is those powerful earthquakes, lasting for five to ten minutes, that cause huge damage if they occur where humans live.

The shock of a large earthquake can sometimes be felt hundreds of miles away. In 1985, a large earthquake in Mexico made water splash out of swimming pools 1000 miles away in Houston, Texas.

Some parts of the world are more prone to earthquakes than others. By far the most earthquakes happen in the "ring of fire" which circles the Pacific Ocean. Others occur in the "Alpine Belt" which stretches from Spain, right through Europe and on to the Himalaya mountains and Southeast Asia. The middle of the Atlantic Ocean is another earthquake area, but deep under the sea.

The power of an earthquake, or its "magnitude", is measured by an instrument called a **seismograph**. This uses the **Richter Scale** as a measurement unit. Each number on this scale, starting with 1, is ten times more powerful than the number below. So an earthquake measuring 4 on the Richter Scale is 10 times more powerful than one measuring 3. An earthquake measuring 7 has about the same power as a megaton nuclear bomb. The highest recorded earthquake measurement so far was 8.9 on the coast of Colombia in 1906.

A SEISMOGRAPH

INVESTIGATING EARTHQUAKES

You will be working with a small group of your classmates to investigate where and why earthquakes happen. You will look at the effects they can have on the lives of human beings, and how the risks of injury from them can be reduced by careful design of buildings and other structures. You will be working as if you were a planning and development team within a large construction corporation. Your team will be using real earthquake data and have to work within a realistic budget. At the end you will present your own carefully designed plan for a part of a building in an earthquake zone.

To do this you will need to:

Learn where and why earthquakes happen.

Understand how earthquakes are measured and can be predicted.

Design, make and test a building structure to see if it could survive an earthquake.

Discover how building design and construction can reduce the risks of damage and injury due to earthquakes.

TEAM-WORK within your group and between other groups of students is going to be very important. You will have to depend upon the work of others and in turn they will be relying on you.

Before you start you will need to do some preparation (a few days ahead of time.) Find a good way to record what you do.

Look carefully at buildings in your area. Assess what you think would happen to them in earthquake conditions.

Make a list of those buildings that you think are most likely to survive a moderate earthquake. Note the features they have that you think makes them likely survivors.

Be ready to get information and ideas from other sources such as:

Libraries for resource books and past newspaper and magazine reports about earthquakes.

The US Geological Survey.

Good maps of the world and the North American continent.

Anyone with professional knowledge that may be able to help your investigations (such as geologists and geographers.)

Use your teacher as a consultant if you need advice.

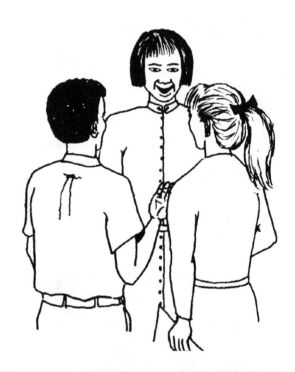

Everyone in your class needs to help to build a collection of earthquake-related resource materials.

GOOD LUCK WITH INVESTIGATING EARTHQUAKES!

SETTING THE SCENE

Throughout this module your group is going to take on a role. You will be a planning and development team working for a major building design company. This memo has just arrived from the company's chief executive officer. Read it carefully to ensure that you fully understand your job:

CMC Building Design
Internal Memo

To: All planning and development teams
From: The Chief Executive Officer

A review of our design work over the last two years has just been done. It shows that we have never won a major building contract in cities that are located in earthquake-prone areas.

We also are aware of a number of contract bids coming out looking for development plans by cities in earthquake zones, especially on the Pacific Rim.

These cities need to be earthquake conscious as they grow. They are looking for development plans that provide for the safety of their citizens and visitors, as well as the more usual needs. Contracts like this will help our company to grow. Everyone in the company stands to benefit from this new business.

In order to successfully compete for these contracts in the Pacific Rim, we must build up our knowledge about construction in earthquake zones. As Chief Executive, I have decided to make this the top priority task for all planning and development teams. Your teams will therefore begin your research immediately.

To help you in your task, I am providing you with a series of Activity Guides. Toward the end, each team will be responsible for designing and testing a different building component. The results will form a presentation to the Executive Board. This should make everyone aware of all the issues.

Because this is a special priority program, we must control the costs of the research and development. Your team will work within a budget which must not be exceeded. The budget details are attached to this memo. Please note that you must calculate the costs of every aspect of your work.

Good luck with your assignment. I look forward to receiving the results.

GARY G. BAGGIO - Chief Executive Officer

CMC Building Design
EARTHQUAKE DEVELOPMENT PROJECT
BUDGET FOR EACH PLANNING AND DEVELOPMENT TEAM

LINE ITEM	DESCRIPTION	BUDGET	ACTUAL	BALANCE
	Salary and Fringe			
71103	Salaries	1,000		
71104	Fringes (Health insurance etc.)	250		
Total		**1,250**		
	Consultants			
82201	Fees	150		
Total		**150**		
	Travel			
73004	Travel	500		
Total		**500**		
	Research and Development			
54302	Data searches	100		
84221	Materials	100		
74331	Report preparation	100		
Total		**300**		
Total Expenses		**2,200**		

NOTES:

This budget shows you how much money your team has to spend on the entire project. This is what the different categories mean in the budget:

line item: - a number that tells your accounting department what you are spending money for
description: - tells you what the line item stands for in plain English
budget: - how much money you have available to spend in a particular category
actual: - how much money you spent in a particular category
balance: - how much money you have left after you have spent some of it from that category.

Keeping track of your spending: You will need to set up an accounting book. In this you can record all expenses so that you can keep a record of what you have. Here is an example for one line item:

Line item: 82201		Description: Consultants	
Date	**Description**	**Amount spent**	**Balance remaining**
April 12	Jones, David	150	350
May 23	Ortega, Jose	200	150

Notice that each time you pay somebody, you have to subtract the amount paid from the balance. You only have a total of $500 to spend on consultants. If this was your budget you would have only $150 left to spend on consulting fees, after paying David Jones and Jose Ortega.

WHERE DO EARTHQUAKES OCCUR MOST OFTEN?

Earthquakes do not happen everywhere. Some places have earthquakes more frequently than others. Working as a planning and development team for a major building design corporation, you need to find out where earthquake zones are. In particular, you need to find places in these zones where major cities and towns already exist. This activity will provide you with useful information that will help your planning effort.

You are going to work in a group of 4 or 5 students.

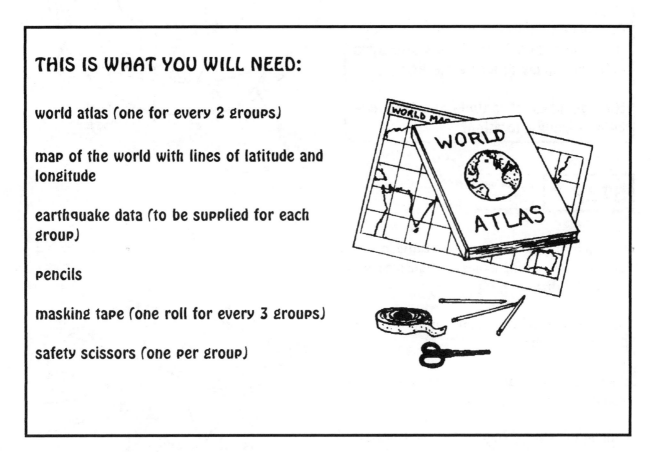

THIS IS WHAT YOU WILL NEED:

world atlas (one for every 2 groups)

map of the world with lines of latitude and longitude

earthquake data (to be supplied for each group)

pencils

masking tape (one roll for every 3 groups)

safety scissors (one per group)

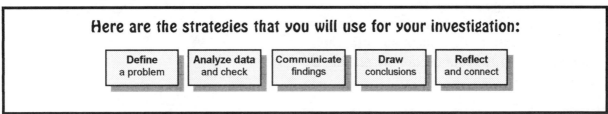

Here are the strategies that you will use for your investigation:

| Define a problem | Analyze data and check | Communicate findings | Draw conclusions | Reflect and connect |

Your teacher will help you to divide into groups of about four.

Look at the world map. Find the lines of latitude and longitude. Make sure you know which is which.

Ask yourselves
these questions:

> **What earthquakes do you already know about?**
>
> **Approximately where on the map would these be located? (Use the world atlas index and maps to locate places.)**
>
> **How do lines of latitude and longitude help in fixing a location?**

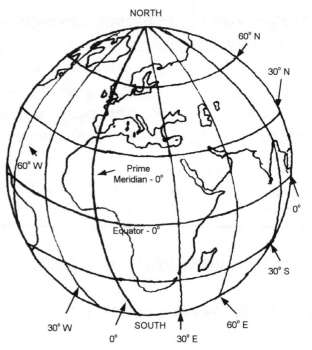

STEP 2 | Define a problem

Take the map of the world and divide it into four parts by cutting along the Equator and the Prime Meridian.

Each member of your team can now take one section of the map.

Note which lines of latitude and longitude are included in each map section.

Look at the US Geological Survey data (shown on the next page.) This shows where the epicenter (or center) of known earthquakes has taken place. Plot the location of each earthquake listed for your section by placing a pencil dot on the map.

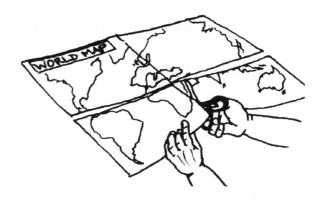

This data chart shows places where earthquakes have taken place. Their locations are fixed by using a latitude and longitude grid reference. Latitude lines run around the globe. The Equator is 0 degrees (0^0) latitude. Latitude lines begin with the equator and increase in number toward the North and South Poles.

Longitude lines go across latitude lines to make the grid. They all connect to both the North and South poles (looking a bit like a peeled orange's segments.) O degrees is on the Prime Meridian which passes from the North Pole through Greenwich in London, England, and then on to the South Pole. Longitude lines are numbered to east and west of this meridian. Latitude and longitude are measurement systems that are universally accepted. With them any point on the Earth can be given a reference. Ships and airplanes depend on them for navigation.

SOME EARTHQUAKE EPICENTERS									
Lat.	Long.	Lat.	Long.	Lat.	Long.	Lat.	Long.	Lat.	Long.
52N	73W	14N	45E	5S	102E	31S	77E	16N	145E
56N	163E	7S	128E	6S	155E	21S	68W	20S	179W
37N	35E	12N	126E	6S	154E	56N	162E	44N	138E
7S	147E	19N	155W	17N	93W	18N	147E	54N	168E
25N	123E	44N	75W	14S	13W	41S	89W	60N	160E
27N	45W	18S	178W	7N	34W	51N	179W	34N	136E
18S	173W	7N	94E	38N	16E	4S	106W	6N	77W
43N	17E	41S	86W	1N	126E	7S	125E	1N	91W
16S	168E	43N	147E	7N	94E	42N	144E	7N	73W
36N	68E	27N	56E	27N	100E	30S	179W	68N	19W
21S	66E	59S	18W	39N	143E	32S	178W	5S	145E
45S	168E	17S	173W	4S	77W	20S	68W	52N	176W
17N	100W	36N	53E	51N	175E	43N	127W	49N	124W
46N	11E	20N	110W	49N	124W	52N	131W	54S	141E
66N	11E	20N	109W	22S	169E	4S	12W	54S	142E
14S	67E	4N	104W	12S	167E	57N	25W	26S	27E
44N	10E	8S	114E	21S	179W	8N	40W	13S	167E
25N	92E	52N	176E	7N	127E	18S	174W	63S	158W
37N	72E	49N	154E	10S	119E	19N	155W	41N	124W
42S	172	38N	70E	45N	129W	38N	141E	52N	173W

STEP 3 | Analyze data and check

When all the epicenters have been located on the four map sections, put the sections back together again. You can use tape on the back of the map to do this.

Look closely at the map, and ask these questions:

What patterns can you find?

What does this tell you about where earthquakes happen?

Where do they not seem to happen?

What parts of the world seem to be earthquake zones? (You can mark these on your maps.)

STEP 4 | Draw conclusions

Consult your world atlas. This will show major cities and towns.

By comparing your world map with the atlas, find any major cities and towns which are located within earthquake zones.

Mark some of these, from around the world, onto your world map.

When you have a sense of the world earthquake zones, look especially for those cities which are found on the Pacific Rim. This includes North and South America, China, Japan, and other parts of Southeast Asia. Mark these carefully on your map.

STEP 5 | Draw conclusions | Communicate findings

Using any resource materials (books, magazines, old newspaper reports) that you can collect, find out all you can about earthquakes that have happened in any of these cities.

When you have found out all you can, have a presentation session where each group shares its information with everyone else.

STEP 6 | Analyze data and check

Your team must now figure out what you have spent so far.

Total up each line item cost and calculate the balance still not spent.

Here are some costs to factor in:

($$) BUDGET ACCOUNT

ITEMS	$ COSTS
Materials	
pencils	0.10 each
map	2.00 each
scissors	1.00 each
Atlas	20.00 each
tape	1.00 roll
Salaries	
@ $10 per person hour	?
Fringe	
@ 25% of salaries	?

CONCLUSIONS | Draw conclusions

Work with your teacher to reach some general conclusions. You will need to analyze the evidence you have collected.

Here are key questions to consider:

What possible reasons can you think of that might explain why earthquakes only happen in some parts of the world?

What reasons might there be to explain why cities are built in earthquake zones?

REFLECTIONS | Reflect and connect

What evidence does this activity provide for answering the BIG question: **What are the causes and effects of earthquakes?**

ACTIVITY 2

HOW DO WE EXPLAIN EARTHQUAKE PATTERNS?

You have found out that earthquakes take place in certain parts of the world. But why are earthquake zones found where they are? What is it which causes the earth to quake in these places? In order to continue your planning and development task successfully, you need to find answers to these questions.

You are going to work in a group of about 4 students.

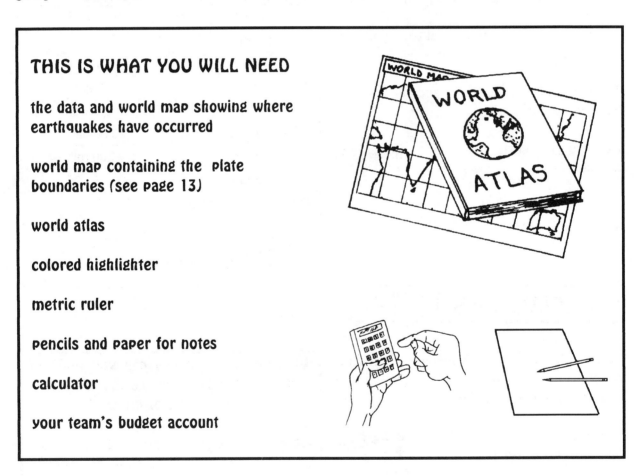

THIS IS WHAT YOU WILL NEED

the data and world map showing where earthquakes have occurred

world map containing the plate boundaries (see page 13)

world atlas

colored highlighter

metric ruler

pencils and paper for notes

calculator

your team's budget account

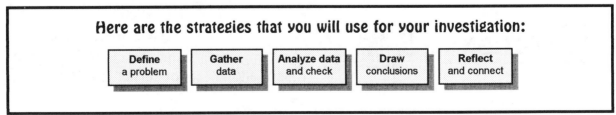

Here are the strategies that you will use for your investigation:

| Define a problem | Gather data | Analyze data and check | Draw conclusions | Reflect and connect |

With your team, study the world map showing the plate boundaries.

Compare this new map with the world map on which you plotted known earthquakes.

Use your highlighter pen to mark the plate boundaries onto your earthquake map. Be sure that your lines are about 1 cm. thick.

What do you notice? Is there a possible connection?

This special note will help you answer these questions:

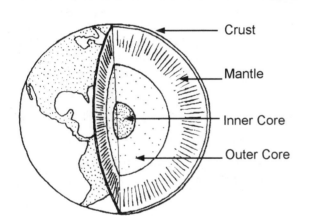

SPECIAL NOTE ABOUT PLATE BOUNDARIES

Earth's outer layer is made up of rock. This CRUST varies in thickness from between 5 to 30 km. It is broken into several large pieces called PLATES. There are six main plates and six smaller ones.

Movements are constantly occurring in the layer beneath the Earth's crust, called the MANTLE. The mantle is made of rock which is so hot it is partly molten, especially just below the crust. The plates float on the mantle which makes them move. Most movement happens at plate boundaries or margins. This is where different plates collide, separate, or slide past each other.

To further understand how this works you should consult resource books about earthquakes.

- - - - - Plate boundaries

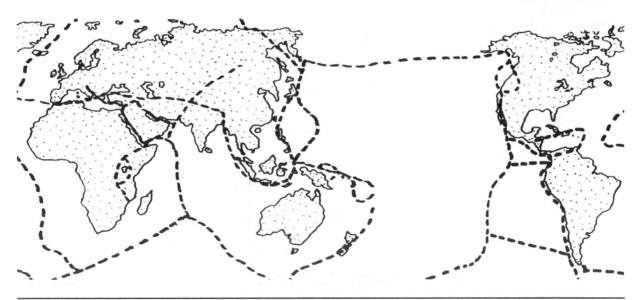

You can check this connection by calculating some interesting percentages.

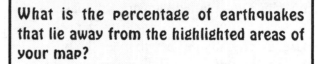
What is the percentage of earthquakes you have plotted that lie within, or very near, the highlighted areas of your map?

What is the percentage of earthquakes that lie away from the highlighted areas of your map?

What is the percentage of earthquakes that occur along the boundaries that circle the coast of the Pacific Ocean?

What is the percentage that occur along boundaries located in inland areas?

To calculate percentages count the total number of reported earthquakes (TE). Next count the number of earthquakes there are in category (EQ). Divide EQ by TE and multiply by 100.

Here is the formula: $$EQ \times \frac{100}{TE} = category\ \%$$

STEP 3 Analyze data and check | Communicate findings

Hold a review meeting in which each group in turn presents its percentage calculations.

TEAM	EARTHQUAKES CLOSE TO BOUNDARIES	EARTHQUAKES AWAY FROM BOUNDARIES	EARTHQUAKES ON PACIFIC BOUNDARY	EARTHQUAKES FOUND IN INLAND AREAS	AVERAGE %
A					
B		You can compare your results by making a combined results chart like this.			
C					
D					

STEP 4 | Draw conclusions

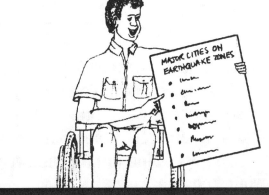

Based on this evidence, make a new list of cities in the Pacific Rim that lie within earthquake zones.

How does it compare with the first list your team made?

STEP 5 | Analyze data and check

Your team must now work out what you have spent so far.

Total up each line item cost and calculate the balance still not spent.

Here are more costs to factor in.

($$) BUDGET ACCOUNT

ITEMS	$ COSTS
Materials	
map	2.00 each
calculator	10.00 each
highlighter	0.50 each
ruler	2.00 each
Salaries	
@ $10 per person hour	?
Fringe	
@ 25% of salaries	?

CONCLUSIONS | Draw conclusions

Work with your teacher to reach some general conclusions. You will need to analyze the evidence you have collected.

Here are key questions to consider:

What do you think is the connection between earthquake activity and plate boundaries?

Why do you think that there are very few earthquakes in the middle of plates?

REFLECTIONS | Reflect and connect

What evidence does this activity provide for answering the BIG question: **What are the causes and effects of earthquakes?**

You know that earthquakes are most likely to happen in zones where the boundary plates of the Earth's crust meet. But why do they occur and what actually happens when they do? To find out, you and your team are going to do library research. When you have found out most of the information you need, you are going to hire the services of an expert to help you fill in gaps in your knowledge.

You are going to work in a group of about 4 students.

THIS IS WHAT YOU WILL NEED

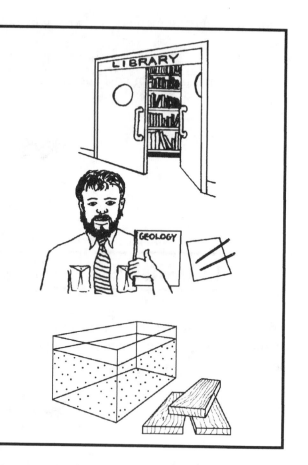

fish tank, sink or washing bowl and water (2 per class)

variety of pieces of different types of wood

access to library resources and materials on plate tectonics, including computer search facility if possible

an expert consultant

pencils and paper for notes

your team's budget account

Here are the strategies that you will use for your investigation:

| Find information | Use models & simulations | Define a problem | Analyze data and check | Draw conclusions | Reflect and connect |

STEP 1 | Use models & simulations

You are going to investigate what happens at the boundaries of the Earth's crust. To get started, spend a few moments observing what happens with pieces of floating wood.

Make sure you have a variety of pieces of wood. They should be of different sizes (and densities.)

What happens when they collide? Do some behave differently from others?

Make notes of your observations.

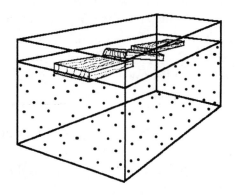

STEP 2 | Define a problem

Your mission is to find as much information as you can about WHY earthquakes happen. To do this you first will need to find out exactly what plate tectonics is.

You will do a library or computer search to find as many sources of information as you can. (NOTE: you may also be able to use public libraries in your community, the local high school or community college library or books you have at home.)

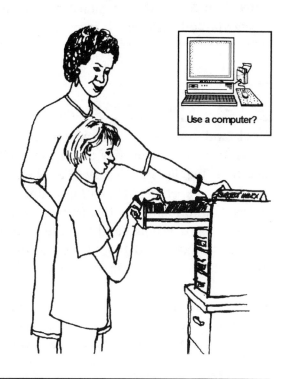

Use a computer?

NOTE ABOUT PLATE TECTONICS
Plate tectonics is a theory, developed by scientists in the 1960s, which explains how crust is created and destroyed.

The edges of the Earth's crust plates are called "margins". New crust flows out from the mid ocean ridges and pushes the old crust of the sea floor under the continents at the ocean trenches. The margins of the plates grinding past each other give the earthquakes.

NOTE ABOUT LIBRARY SEARCHES
Libraries have a system for conducting an information search about a particular topic. The librarian and library staff will know how to do this. Take their advice.

STEP 3 — Find information

From your first library search you will find that plate tectonics involves a number of important scientific topics and ideas. You will need to make a list of these. You will also need to decide how you are going to use your team time effectively.

Should you all work together looking at everything? Would it be more cost-effective if you divide up the tasks, with each member researching a different aspect?

Remember: Time is money as far as your budget is concerned!

SPECIAL NOTE

Here are some key words that you need to look out for in your library research:

* EARTHQUAKE FOCUS *
* SHOCK WAVES *
* AFTER SHOCKS * ENERGY *
* OCEANIC PLATES *
* CONTINENTAL PLATES *
* MAGMA * SPREADING *
* SUBDUCTION *
* COLLISION * FAULTING *
* ACCRETION * HOT SPOTS *

Decide how you are going to organize your information gathering. You need to decide how you are going to share all the information with each other. Once you have an agreed-upon plan, put it into operation! Remember to record the time you spend.

STEP 4 — Define a problem

Book and computer research will give you some answers. But it may also raise further questions that are not so easy to answer. This is where a expert can be helpful. Unlike print or visual information, with an expert you can keep asking questions until you are sure that you fully understand the answers. You can also check that your ideas are correct.

With your team members, discuss the actual questions you need to ask the consultant. **Prepare your list of questions carefully.**

Get together with the other planning and development teams. You are all going to share the consultant. Review all the questions and produce a new overall list. When you are fully prepared, arrange a time for the consultant's visit.

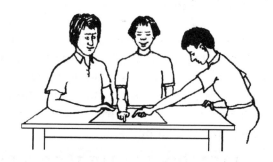

$$$$ SHARE THE COSTS!

Expert consultants can be expensive! But if you are all going to benefit from him or her it can be a saving. For example, if 20 of you are library searching for 2 hours, that costs $10 X 20 X 2 = $400. A consultant costs just $100. You save! But this is only true if you use his or her time profitably. To get good value you need to be prepared. It is wasteful if the consultant answers questions where the answers are readily available elsewhere.

STEP 5 | Find information

Consult your expert!

Be sure to take notes of the information your consultant gives you.

STEP 6 | Analyze data and check

Your team must now figure out what you have spent so far.

Total up each line item cost and calculate the balance still not spent.

Here are some more costs to factor in.

($$) BUDGET ACCOUNT

ITEMS	$ COSTS
Materials	
Water container & wood	10.00
Consultant fee	
@ $50 per hour	(your share of the cost)
Salaries	
@ $10 per person hour	?
Fringe	
@ 25% of salaries	?

CONCLUSIONS | Draw conclusions

Work with your teacher to reach some general conclusions. You will need to analyze the evidence you have collected.

Here are key questions to consider:

How well do you understand the science involved with earthquakes?

What more do you think you need to know?

How is research important in science?

REFLECTIONS | Reflect and connect

What evidence does this activity provide for answering the BIG question: **What are the causes and effects of earthquakes?**

ACTIVITY 4 | HOW ARE WAVES INVOLVED WITH EARTHQUAKES?

Your research will have shown you that earthquakes happen because waves of energy are released when rocks suddenly slip along a fault zone in the Earth's crust. But how do these shock waves transfer the energy to the Earth's surface? Your team will now investigate waves, and how they behave. This will help you to understand the effects shock waves can have on buildings and other structures.

You are going to work in a group of about 4 students.

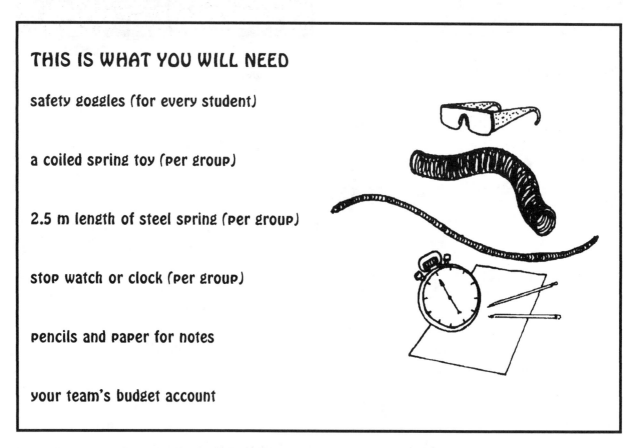

THIS IS WHAT YOU WILL NEED

safety goggles (for every student)

a coiled spring toy (per group)

2.5 m length of steel spring (per group)

stop watch or clock (per group)

pencils and paper for notes

your team's budget account

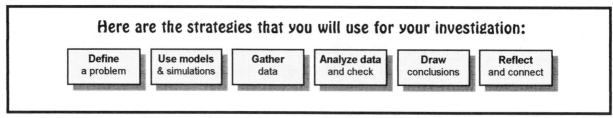

Here are the strategies that you will use for your investigation:

Define a problem	Use models & simulations	Gather data	Analyze data and check	Draw conclusions	Reflect and connect

The transfer of energy through waves is the key to understanding the effects of earthquakes.

Here are some brief details of how waves are involved with earthquakes:

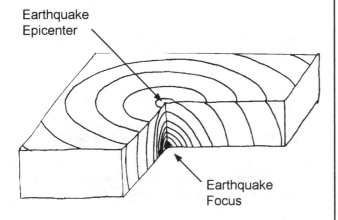

Earthquake Epicenter

Earthquake Focus

To help your understanding, your team is going to produce and measure some waves.

SAFETY NOTE:
WEAR SAFETY GOGGLES

Use the coiled spring toy. Have two of your team each hold the spring toy, one at each end. Stretch it about three meters on the floor.

Have one person gather about 5 of the coils of the spring toy. When ready, release these coils and watch the waves of energy that are produced.

Do it again, but this time have another person measure the length of time the coils are in motion after they have been released. The fourth person can record the results.

To get an accurate reading, do this test four times and average the results.

NOTE ABOUT SEISMIC WAVES
From your earlier research you discovered that the ENERGY from the source of an earthquake (or its EPICENTER) is transferred outward by shock waves, called SEISMIC WAVES.

The concept of "waves" is important in science. It explains how many types of energy transfer take place, including: sound and light. Shock waves in an earthquake behave in the same way.

One way to think about how waves behave is to recall what happens when you drop a stone into water. Waves ripple out in an even fashion from the point where the stone hits the water.

Three types of waves are created during an earthquake: COMPRESSIONAL (Primary,) SHEAR (Secondary,) and LOVE (Surface.)

The Love waves, that travel along the surface of the crust, cause damage to cities and people.

Use models & simulations | Gather data

STEP 2 | Use models & simulations | Gather data

Repeat the same test, but this time gather 20 coils. Record the time of the motion as before. **Then repeat once more using 40 gathered coils. (Remember to do each test 4 times and average the results to get a final measurement.)**

Use a data-chart like this to record your results:

COILED TOY WAVES TEST					
# of coils	Test 1 motion time	Test 2 motion time	Test 3 motion time	Test 4 motion time	Average motion time
5					
20					
40					

STEP 3 | Use models & simulations | Gather data

To model secondary waves use the 2.5 m. coiled steel spring. As before, have two people hold each end. Hold it out along the floor but do not stretch it beyond its normal length.

Have one of the spring holders swing his or her hand up and down for about 30 cm. Have the time keeper and recorder repeat their jobs. Remember to repeat the test 4 times and average the results.

Increase the height of the swing, first to 45 cm. and then to 60 cm. and take readings as before.

To simulate the motion of Love waves (surface waves,) use the steel spring again.

This time have the holders stand up. Have one person swing his or her end up and down, first at about 30 cm, then at 45 cm. and last at 65 cm.

As before, have the timekeeper and recorder do their jobs.

STEEL SPRING SECONDARY WAVES TEST					
Width of swing	Test 1 motion time	Test 2 motion time	Test 3 motion time	Test 4 motion time	Average motion time
30 cm.					
45 cm.					
60 cm.					

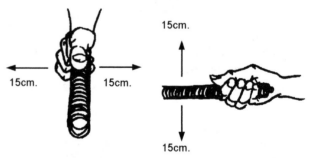

STEEL SPRING SURFACE WAVES TEST					
Width of swing	Test 1 motion time	Test 2 motion time	Test 3 motion time	Test 4 motion time	Average motion time
30 cm.					
45 cm.					
60 cm.					

STEP 4 | Analyze data and check

Now study all your data and ask yourselves these questions:

What relationships and patterns can you find between the amount of energy put into the springs and the length of time they were in motion? If so, how can you explain them?

What do you think this might mean about the earthquake waves that have different strengths?

STEP 5 | Analyze data and check

Your team must now figure out what you have spent so far.

Total up each line item cost and calculate the balance still not spent.

Here are some more costs to factor in.

($$) BUDGET ACCOUNT

ITEMS	$ COSTS
Materials	
spring	5.00
coiled spring toy	5.00
stop watch	5.00
goggles	5.00
Salaries	
@ $10 per person hour	?
Fringe	
@ 25% of salaries	?

CONCLUSIONS | Draw conclusions

Work with your teacher to reach some general conclusions. You will need to analyze the evidence you have collected.

Here are key questions to consider:

What part do waves play in causing damage to the surface of the Earth?

How does an understanding of the energy transfer through waves help us to understand earthquakes?

REFLECTIONS | Reflect and connect

What evidence does this activity provide for answering the BIG question: **What are the causes and effects of earthquakes?**

WHAT PATTERNS OF DAMAGE CAN EARTHQUAKES CAUSE?

The effects of some earthquakes can be devastating. This is especially so when they occur in areas where people live. Over the years there have been some highly destructive earthquakes. One of the earliest known was in Lisbon, capital city of Portugal, in November 1755. About 60,000 people died that day. But not all these deaths happened in the same way. With most life threatening earthquakes there is a pattern of destruction and a chain of events.

You are going to work in a group of about 4 students.

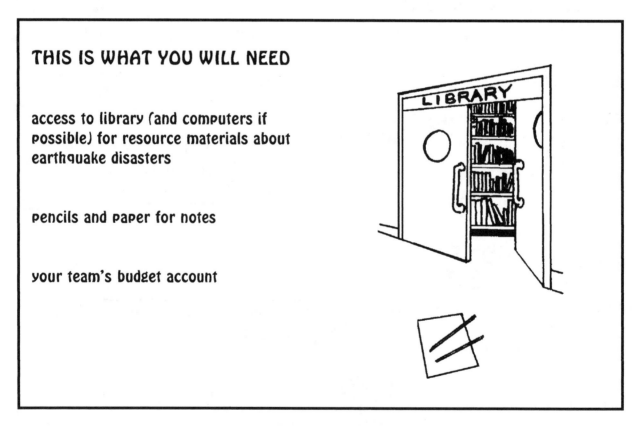

THIS IS WHAT YOU WILL NEED

access to library (and computers if possible) for resource materials about earthquake disasters

pencils and paper for notes

your team's budget account

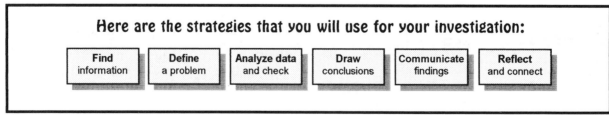

Here are the strategies that you will use for your investigation:

| Find information | Define a problem | Analyze data and check | Draw conclusions | Communicate findings | Reflect and connect |

STEP 1	Find information

HOW TO GO ABOUT IT

Once again you will need to search your library for information.

This time you are looking for details of any major earthquakes that have taken place. In particular, you will be looking for reports of what happened.

Here are some well known earthquakes that have occurred during the 20th Century:

➡️

Try to find out as much information about them as you can. Concentrate on the sequence of events: what happened first, then what happened next, and so on.

SOME TWENTIETH CENTURY EARTHQUAKES		
Date	**Place**	**Deaths**
1908	Italy	160.000
1920	China	180,000
1923	Japan	143,000
1935	India	60,000
1939	Turkey	40,000
1960	Morocco	12,000
1970	Peru	50,000
1972	Nicaragua	12,000
1976	China	700,000
1976	Guatemala	23,000
1988	Armenia	55,000
1990	Iran	35,000

STEP 2	Analyze data and check

When you have gathered as much information as you can, look for patterns.

➡️

Here are questions to guide you:

What is the sequence of events in an earthquake?

What sequence of experiences do people have when a city experiences a serious earthquake?

What are the major causes of fatalities and injury when a city earthquake takes place?

As you know, earthquake strength is measured using a seismograph, on the Richter Scale.

The highest earthquakes that have occurred (measured on the Richter Scale) have not necessarily caused major fatalities. This is because they have not always taken place where people live, but in unpopulated areas.

Another way of measuring the effects of earthquakes was developed by a seismologist called Mercalli. In this scale the effects on humans and cities is used.

Study this scale and ask yourself what it tells you about the pattern of events when an earthquake happens.

THE MERCALLI SCALE	
0	Movement registered only by seismographs.
I	Felt by only a few people, perhaps lying on hard ground.
II	Felt by people in bed, especially in tall buildings
III	Felt by many people indoors. Hanging objects begin to swing.
IV	Felt generally indoors. Parked cars rock, crockery rattles, walls crack.
V	Felt indoors and outside. Some people awakened. Objects fall over, trees shake. Some glass may break. At this level the vibrations and noises are for the first time recognized as an earthquake.
VI	Felt by all. Furniture moves. Roof tiles fall. Difficult to walk.
VII	Everyone hurries outside. Difficult to stand up. Buildings start to collapse - light damage in well-built buildings, but serious damage in poorly-constructed ones.
VIII	Panic. Difficult to drive. Factory chimneys, monuments and walls fall down. All windows break. Tree branches break. Cracks appear in the ground, and sand and mud spurt out. The level and temperature of water in wells changes.
IX	General panic. Most buildings collapse partially or totally. Large cracks appear in the ground.
X	Dams break, flooding from lakes and rivers. Landslides. Railroad lines twisted.
XI	Underground pipes break. Few or no buildings survive. Valleys fill with mud from landslides or are flooded.
XII	Total disaster. Towns razed to the ground. Large waves in the ground. Objects thrown into the air. Uncontrollable panic.

STEP 4 | Analyze data and check | Communicate findings

Now focus on ways in which you think some of these fatality risks could be reduced.

To save salary costs, have each team take responsibility for a different risk.

When each team has discussed some likely risk reducers, hold an open discussion. Each group in turn can present its ideas.

Here are some risk factors to consider:

Fatality or injury	Cause of fatality or injury
Falling	People falling from buildings and other high structures
Being hit	Falling objects from buildings
Crushed	From building collapse
Buried	Suffocating or dying under rubble from collapsed buildings
Drowned	From tidal waves or dam bursts
Burned	By fires caused by earthquake, fractured gas tanks, electrical shocks.
Diseased	From polluted water supply and lack of sanitation
Suffocated	By smoke or gas from fractured pipes and tanks.

STEP 5 | Analyze data and check

Your team must now figure out what you have spent so far.

($$) BUDGET ACCOUNT

ITEMS	$ COSTS
Salaries	
@ $10 per person hour	?
Fringe	
@ 25% of salaries	?

CONCLUSIONS | Draw conclusions

Work with your teacher to reach some general conclusions. You will need to analyze the evidence you have collected.

Here are key questions to consider:

What are the most likely causes of death when a serious earthquake happens?

How could the design of buildings and other structures minimize the risks of injury and death in an earthquake?

REFLECTIONS | Reflect and connect

What evidence does this activity provide for answering the BIG question: **What are the causes and effects of earthquakes?**

CAN THE RISKS OF EARTHQUAKE DAMAGE BE REDUCED?

If we cannot prevent earthquakes from happening, what can be done to minimize the risks to humans and the buildings they occupy? Today, seismologists, scientists who study movements in the Earth's crust, have learned a great deal about earthquakes. Their observations and measurements can sometimes help them to predict where earthquakes may happen. Buildings and other structures can be designed to cope better with tremors and shock waves caused by earthquakes. Emergency services and systems can be developed to swing into action at the first signs of an earthquake alert. But how are building designs tested before they are built?

You are going to work in a group of about 4 students.

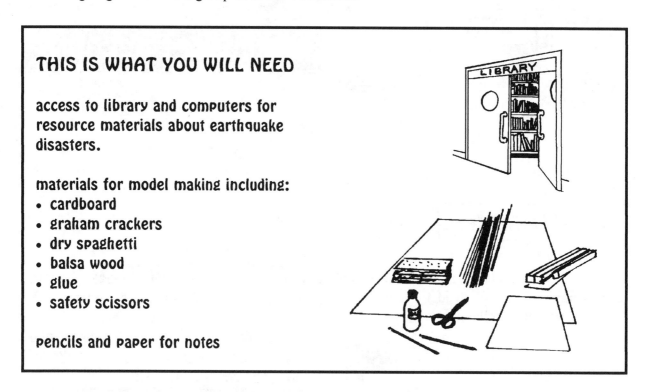

THIS IS WHAT YOU WILL NEED

access to library and computers for resource materials about earthquake disasters.

materials for model making including:
- cardboard
- graham crackers
- dry spaghetti
- balsa wood
- glue
- safety scissors

pencils and paper for notes

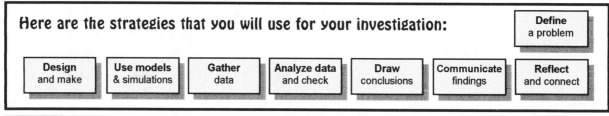

Here are the strategies that you will use for your investigation:

						Define a problem
Design and make	Use models & simulations	Gather data	Analyze data and check	Draw conclusions	Communicate findings	Reflect and connect

An obvious way to protect lives and prevent injury from earthquakes is to avoid the construction of buildings in earthquake zones at all. But this can be very difficult and also very expensive. Imagine trying to move everyone out of San Francisco to a new San Francisco in another part of the country!

Predicting earthquakes also helps. If there is enough warning time, people can get away from buildings to safe areas before the earthquake hits. But seismology is a young science and it is still very difficult to make accurate predictions. Research needed is also very expensive.

Since most of the immediate deaths in earthquakes happen because of building collapse, there are two possibilities:

1   design the building so that it will absorb the shock waves;

2   make the buildings from materials that are lightweight, causing less injury to people when the buildings collapse.

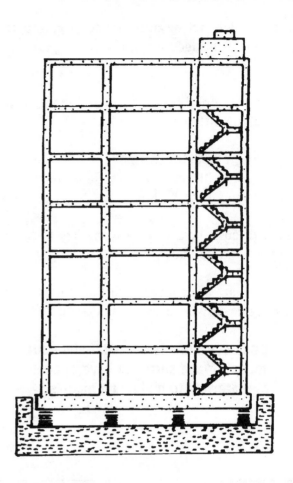

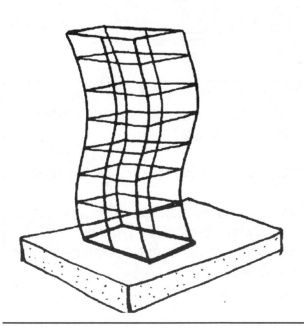

Architects and engineers designing buildings or bridges need to test how they will stand up to earthquakes. Obviously, they cannot do this with the real thing. Instead, they have to conduct design tests before construction begins.

There are several ways this can be done. One way is to build a model of the structure and test it. Another is to test parts of the real building before it is put together (such as door frames, ceiling beams or a foundation pile.)

Tests can also be done using computer simulations. These have been developed by studying all the data that have been collected about how structures behave during actual earthquakes.

Your planning and development team is going to design, make and test a model.

The model can be a complete structure (a building or bridge for example,) or a part of a building.

It will be helpful if each team builds and tests something different.

Building a model is cost-effective. So the first thing you will need to do is figure out what each team will test.

First discuss ideas in your team. Try to list a number of alternatives.

Next, share your ideas with the other teams and agree on what each team is going to do.

Once everyone is agreed, build your model. Make sure you have enough materials to make two models.

TESTING STRUCTURAL DESIGN

Design involves both shape and materials. The strength of structures depends on the combining of both these things. It is possible to make a strong building from quite weak materials with careful design. For example, a tent will stay up in very high winds, yet its materials are very lightweight.

You will need to consider these two aspects carefully when making your models. Try to find materials that behave like real building materials. For example, dried spaghetti behaves like wooden poles, graham crackers behave like slabs of concrete. You will need to justify the materials you use.

To test the models you will need to design an earthquake simulator. Perhaps one team can take responsibility for this, to ensure that the tests are fair. (Consult with your teacher).

 STEP 2 | Use models & simulations | Gather data | Analyze data and check |

Using the earthquake simulator, your model will be tested to destruction. You must closely observe how it behaves, and note where the weaknesses are. Make sure you record how long it takes for the model to collapse.

Try to find a way to improve your model, and then build a second improved version. Test the model again, in exactly the same way. Note the improvement.

Review your findings using these questions as a guide:

What implications does your model testing have for the design of buildings in earthquake zones?

What evidence is there to support this?

What recommendations can you make to the Chief Executive Officer of CMC Building Design about earthquake zone buildings?

CONCLUSIONS

Draw conclusions
Communicate findings

Now you need to work together with the other planning and development teams. Your task is to prepare your presentation to the Executive Board. Take another look at the Chief Executive Officer's internal memo (page 5) to remind yourself of your original mission. You will need to review all the work you have done and draw out the conclusions you have reached about building in earthquake zones.

Here are questions to guide you:

Make sure your presentation is interesting and informative. Be creative!

What are the major difficulties about constructing buildings in earthquake zones?

What are the likely effects of a major earthquake hitting a city or town?

What can be done to lower the risks of earthquake damage to buildings and humans?

What features do buildings in earthquake prone areas need to have and why?

What evidence has your testing of models produced to inform your presentation?

Give your presentations. See if you can find a way of displaying your work for others to see, e.g. other classes, parents, school visitors.

$ $ $ $ $ FINAL BUDGET ACCOUNTING $ $ $ $ $

Your team must now work out what you have spent on the whole project. You need to do a final set of accounts showing all spending for all line items.

Have you managed to stay within your budget? Do you have any surplus funds?

FINAL REFLECTIONS

Reflect and connect

What evidence have you produced that answers the BIG question on page 1:

WHAT ARE THE CAUSES AND EFFECTS OF EARTHQUAKES?

With your team, then with the entire class, evaluate the whole module. Try to assess what you have learned, and also how you have learned it.

What are the most important points about earthquakes that you now understand?

How did you enjoy the way in which you learned about earthquakes?

What have you learned about "how" you learn?

This investigation may be over, but it will not be the end of the story! Look out for news reports about earthquakes. Try to pass on your knowledge to others.

A range of sensitive instruments are used to measure small movements in the Earth's crust. The data collected from these are analyzed by scientists looking for patterns and relationships that may help with earthquake prediction.

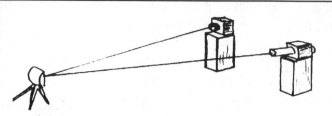

Lasers can be used to detect movements and changes in the Earth's surface.

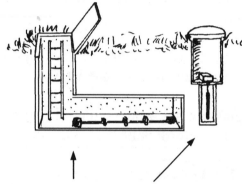

Strainmeters and creepmeters are used to detect movements in the Earth.

The water level in wells can change when an earthquake is about to happen.

In recent years much research has been carried out by seismologists, especially in China, Japan, and the U.S., all countries where earthquakes happen. But it is still difficult to predict major earthquakes accurately. Small tremors are sometimes followed by larger ones, but not always. Most really large earthquakes happen without any warning.

Seismographs are used to pick up the energy waves from earthquakes. These have a base which shakes with an earthquake and a pen is attached to a hanging weight which remains still. Any movement of the base makes the pen leave a trace on a drum to which graph paper is attached. The drum is really a rotating clock, so a record is made showing any movement that has occurred and the exact time it happened.

A seismograph can detect small shocks that take place deep in the earth. By seeing how long it takes for the waves to arrive on the surface, seismologists can tell how far away the earthquake is and where its epicenter is.

Animal Predictors
Animals can be predictors of earthquakes. They can sense small movements in the earth. The Chinese have studied this and say that before an earthquake, fish become very agitated and small animals like mice and rabbits run around in panic.

Looking for ways to predict major earthquakes has been going on for centuries. In the 2nd century, an instrument for measuring earthquakes was developed.

A pendulum hung in a bronze jar moved when an earthquake happened. This, in turn, made one of the eight dragons on the jar move and a small ball would fall out of its mouth into a toad's mouth below. The toad which caught the ball showed the direction the earthquake had come from.